MW00636812

Hair
Food

Well of Wisdom Publishing House
Los Angeles, CA USA 91506
www.wellofwisdompublishing.com
info@wellofwisdompublishing.com

Hair Food: Recipes to Promote Positive Hair Health and Hair Loss Restoration

Copyright 2022 © Lacy Fields and Charisma McLaughlin. All rights reserved

No part of this book may be reproduced, stored in a retrieval system, or transmitted by any means without the authors' written permission.

Published by Well of Wisdom Publishing House 1/1/2022

ISBN # (Hardcover): 978-1-7370927-4-2
ISBN # (eBook): 978-1-7370927-5-9

Library of Congress Control Number: 2021925506

Hair Food

RECIPES TO PROMOTE
POSITIVE HAIR HEALTH AND
HAIR LOSS RESTORATION

by

LACY FIELDS AND
CHARISMA MCLAUGHLIN

CONTENTS

INTRODUCTION

Hair Loss Remediation grabbed my attention once I started to get many new clients seeking a hairstylist who specialized in healthy hair care. They were lost, confused, and saddened by their hair's health. In 2010, I decided to dive deeper into hair and hair loss science. I sought to learn more about the body's anatomy under the scalp and skin layers. Through my studies and research, I found that our overall body health plays a significant role in the health and strength of our hair. In addition, longstanding medical research shows that our food intake significantly impacts our overall body health. However, most men and women who suffer from hair loss never consider what they're eating. The foods we consume substantially affect our overall health, including our hair, hair follicles, and scalp. Our hair maintains itself from the inside out, and we need an intake of healthy, balanced, and nutritional meals to aid in our hair's health, growth, and strength. Healthy hair starts with a healthy scalp, and a healthy scalp begins with a healthy body and diet.

Healthy hair starts with a healthy scalp, and a healthy scalp begins with a healthy body and diet.

—LACY

With over 11 years of experience in Trichology, I found myself always sharing with my clients what foods to eat, but I never explored specific meals we should eat, how to properly prepare those hair foods, and so much more —until now. As a hairstylist who loves creative cooking, I knew I wanted to do more. I also knew I needed an actual chef's touch and expertise. That's when I enlisted my sister and friend Charisma to help me create this resource for our community.

My relationship with Charisma started in childhood —our fathers were close friends who ironically also shared a passion for food and cooking. They ultimately passed that bond of brotherhood and love for the culinary arts onto their daughters. I remember when Charisma started her cooking career, and the first time, she introduced me to her infamous pasta dish and fresh salad. I was hooked and instantly fell in love with her cooking. Since then, she has become my sister-chef, and I shamelessly look for opportunities to taste more of her unique dishes. Over the years, we have collaborated on several social and business events. Therefore, it was only right to continue in the spirit of sisterhood and collaboration and join forces to create these hair food specialty dishes.

-Lacy

This *Hair Food* journey started with the healthy hair salad.

At the beginning of my career, I mostly catered to hairstylists. My mother was a beautician most of my life, and hair salons basically raised me. Over the years, I witnessed firsthand how desperately hair professionals searched for healthy food options for themselves and their clients.

In 2012, I delivered my famous pasta dish to Lacy's salon. I added a side salad to her order packed with healthy hair vitamins, and the seed for collaboration was sown. That moment marked the beginning of our hair food journey, but our personal story started long before then.

For as long as I can remember, Lacy has been a part of my life. Our sisterhood is rooted in our childhood and a bond shared by our fathers. My earliest memories of our sisterhood are Family Sundays in our youth. Our dads

> **❝**
>
> I've had the privilege of sitting in Lacy's chair countless times, and she's enjoyed endless meals prepared by me.
>
> —CHARISMA

would take us out along with the other children in the family, and we would embark on countless adventures to the movies or a local park. There were so many kids around during that time, and the adults in the family made sure we shared everything. Lacy and I would always share snacks in the movies. We had each other's back at an early age, and that hasn't changed.

As the years went on and we both excelled in our professional careers, we would constantly cross paths in various professional and social circles.

"Have you met Lacy?" is a question I'd often hear and giggle before saying, *"Girl that's my god sister! We've been connected since ponytails and overalls."*

Our hearts and lives have remained closely knitted together. We share many of the same friends and have always shared a common liking for fashion, food, and travel. I've had the privilege of sitting in Lacy's chair countless times, and she's enjoyed endless meals prepared by me. Growing up as god sisters, we were raised to put family first, so collaborating on this project was a no-brainer.

- Charisma

RECIPES

ENVIED GREENS

PREP TIME 30 Minutes **COOK TIME** 45 Minutes

Collard greens are a great food to incorporate into our diets to promote healthy hair. Collard greens provide Vitamin C and natural collagen, which are essential to maintaining our hair's health. Vitamin C helps blood cells circulate, which directly impacts the health of our scalps, and a healthy scalp is one of the most critical keys to positive hair growth and strength. Collards are also an excellent food source for promoting increased calcium in our bodies.

1 Pound of Fresh Collard Greens

32oz of Chicken or Vegetable Broth

2 Fresh Chopped Jalapeno Peppers

2 Turkey Necks (vegans can skip this option)

COOKING STEPS

1. Wash collard greens with warm water and vinegar.

2. In a medium saucepan, bring the broth to a boil.

3. Add the turkey necks to the broth, and cook for 15 minutes.

4. Add the collard greens and thinly chopped jalapeno peppers to the pot and cook for 30-45 minutes.

Chef Charisma's Food Note

Do not overcook your collard greens. When greens are cooked beyond their recommended 30-45 minutes, they lose a lot of their rich nutrition.

CHARISMA'S CABBAGE VEGGIE SLAW

PREP TIME 15 Minutes   **COOK TIME** 15 Minutes

Veggie slaw is a healthy hair superfood containing sulfur, collagen boosters, antioxidants, and anti-fungal properties. This dish will give your hair strength and elasticity, extending the growth phase and ensuring longer, more healthy hair.

9oz Shredded Cabbage With Carrots

Shredded Kale

4 Oz Shiitake Mushrooms

2 Tablespoons Chopped Red Onion

2 Tablespoons Minced Garlic

1 Tablespoon Smoked Paprika

1/2 Tablespoon Pink Sea Salt

Kosher Salt

1/4 Tablespoon Black Pepper

2 Tablespoons Olive Oil

2 Tablespoons Butter

COOKING STEPS

1. Add butter and olive oil to a pan over medium heat.

2. Once the butter is melted, add all your vegetables to the pan and sauté for 15 minutes or until desired tenderness of the vegetable is reached.

3. Remove vegetables from the pan, plate and enjoy!

Memories

Lacy has always been supportive in every way. No matter the occasion, I can count on her to show up. My absolute favorite memory of Lacy is when she pulled up to pick up food in her newly wrapped Jeep with her business on the back window. I don't know who was more excited! Watching her process and seeing her come out on top gave me a different type of motivation. I bask in my sister's victories as if they were my own.

Chef Charisma

BOMBSHELL BEETS

PREP TIME 15 Minutes   COOK TIME 30 Minutes

The hair follicles need nourishment from the inside of our bodies to produce healthy hair strands, and beets are a root that provide essential nutrients to the roots of our hair. Beets provide iron, magnesium, folate, and potassium, which are highly needed to maintain a healthy core.

2-4 Fresh Yellow Or Red Beets

Organic Olive Oil

Dash Of Kosher Salt

Dash Of Pepper

½ Teaspoon Flax Seeds

½ Teaspoon Hemp Seeds

½ Teaspoon Brown Sugar

COOKING STEPS

1. Preheat oven at 350 degrees.

2. In a medium saucepan, bring 2 cups of water to a boil.

3. Add the unpeeled beets into the boiled water, and cook for 15-20 minutes, depending on the size of the beets.

4. Using a serving spoon, remove the beets from the water and place them on a baking sheet.

5. Cut the beets into two halves while still hot.

6. Add kosher salt, hemp seeds, pepper, flax seeds, and brown sugar to the top of your beets. This will create a layer of seasonings and herbs on your beets to give them a rich taste.

7. While still on your baking sheet, place the beets in the oven for 15 minutes.

8. Cook until browned, remove the beets from the oven, and cool before enjoying.

LACY'S LOADED BAKED SWEET POTATO

PREP TIME 15 Minutes   COOK TIME 30-45 Minutes

Have you ever wondered why the inside of a sweet potato looks like hair strands? Imagine that being a visual representation of our hair's elasticity. Hair elasticity represents our hair's overall strength. Sweet potatoes help balance the elasticity in our hair's strands. Baked potatoes are also a great source of Vitamin A which also promotes a healthy scalp, and as a result, promotes healthy hair growth. Remember, healthy hair starts with a healthy scalp, and a healthy scalp starts with a healthy diet. We also paired this delicious baked potato with a pecan dressing. Pecans are a great source of protein, and a diet healthy in protein helps to strengthen our hair's cuticles.

Raw Sweet Potato

Pecans

½ Tablespoon Brown Sugar

1 ½ Tablespoon Olive Butter

2 Teaspoons Of Apiterra Raw Honey

2 Teaspoons Of Lemon

2 Teaspoons Of Ginger

COOKING STEPS

1. Preheat oven at 400 degrees.

2. Next, cleanse the sweet potato.

3. Place the potato on a baking sheet and bake in the oven for 45 minutes.

4. In a saucepan, melt olive butter, brown sugar, and apiterra.

5. Once the mixture is completely melted, add the pecans to the mix.

6. Cook the mixture for another 5 minutes and turn off the fire to allow the mixture to cook.

7. Remove the sweet potato from the oven and allow it to cool for 5-10 minutes.

8. After the sweet potato cools, use a knife to cut a split directly along the middle of the sweet potato.

9. In the split, pour in the pecan dressing.

Memories

My favorite memory of Charisma will always be her starting her cooking career. Her pasta is still untouchable. Watching my close friends love what they do and do what they love brings me so much joy!

Lacy

VERY VEGAN MEATLOAF

....

PREP TIME 15 Minutes **COOK TIME** 30 Minutes

....

The myth about a vegan diet or vegan foods is they have no nutritional value. However, you can't lose when the vegan diet is balanced, and all the necessary and recommended nutrients are supplemented through alternative food choices! Being a vegan is only harmful and compromises the health of our hair if we aren't eating healthy. Make sure each meal serves a purpose with a healthy mind and healthy hair being the goal!

2 Packs of 16oz Beyond Beef

¼ Chopped Red Onion

¼ Chopped Red Pepper

¼ Chopped Green Pepper

¼ Chopped Yellow Pepper

2 cups Gluten-Free Breadcrumbs

½ cup Apple Sauce

½ Barbecue Sauce

2 Tablespoons Hamburger Seasoning

1 Teaspoon Black Pepper

Olive Oil Spray

COOKING STEPS

1. Preheat oven at 375 degrees.

2. Take the two packs of beyond beef and separate the vegan meat into medium-sized crumbles and add them to a mixing bowl.

3. Add your chopped red onions, red peppers, green peppers, and yellow peppers to your mixing bowl and mix the ingredients with your hands.

4. Add your bread crumbs, apple sauce, barbecue sauce, hamburger seasoning, and black pepper to the beyond beef mixture and mix the ingredients.

5. Add the beyond beef mixture to your loaf pan, cover with aluminum foil, and bake in the oven for 30 minutes.

6. Remove the meatloaf from the oven, then remove the foil and two tablespoons of barbecue sauce on the top of the meatloaf.

Serve and enjoy!

Chef Charisma's Food Note

Pair our very vegan meatloaf with any of our side dishes.

RAVISHING RASPBERRY CRUSTED LAMB

....

PREP TIME 30 Minutes   COOK TIME 30 Minutes

....

The raspberry crust on this protein-packed dish is
full of folic acid for hair growth and shine.

1 Lamb Rack

6 oz Fresh Raspberries

1 Tablespoon Olive Oil

**1/2 Cup Breadcrumbs
(gluten-free optional)**

PREP

1. Preheat oven at 400 degrees

2. Line baking sheet with parchment paper.

3. Pat lamb rack dry with paper towels.

4. Cut lamb rack into individual lamb lollipops.

COOKING STEPS

1. Add fresh raspberries to a mixing bowl and gently
   press the berries with the back of a spoon to
   create a paste consistency.

2. Add olive oil, sea salt, and pepper to the lamb
   chops.

3. Add the raspberry paste onto each individual lamb
   chop.

4. Gently press breadcrumbs onto the edge of each
   lamb chop.

5. Place lamb chops on a lined baking sheet.

6. Bake your lamb chops for 20-30 minutes.

7. After 20-30 minutes, remove the lamb chops from
   the oven. Allow to cool, and enjoy!

SULTRY CITRUS SALMON

. . . .

PREP TIME 15 Minutes   **COOK TIME** 15-20 Minutes

. . . .

Salmon is packed with Omega 3 and fatty acids, which both promote hair growth. Citrus fruit also combats oily hair.

2-6 oz Salmon Portions

1 Tablespoon Old Bay Seasoning

1 Citrus Fruit (lemon, lime, or orange)

COOKING STEPS

1. Preheat oven at 350 degrees.

2. Place the salmon on a lined oiled baking sheet, sprinkle with old bay and squeeze your citrus of choice on top of the salmon.

3. Bake for 15-20 mins.

4. After 15-20 minutes, remove the salmon from the oven. Allow to cool, and enjoy!

Daddy's Girls

To say our fathers would be proud of us and the sisterhood we've created would be an understatement. Family isn't always determined by who we share the same blood with. Sometimes, it's more about the people who have always been there or two individuals who share the same life goals and mindsets. Though we are in two different industries, Lacy and I have stayed connected through time and a continuous commitment to support one another in life and our business endeavors. We've created a sisterhood founded on our fathers' friendship that would surely make them proud.

Chef Charisma

Daddy's Girls

Like many fatherless women in the world, we wish our fathers could see who we've become. We didn't grow up in perfect houses with our fathers. However, they ultimately helped us become who we are today. If they saw us today, I believe they would be grateful to know that we have kept our bond over the years. I also think we both exceeded their expectations. We've lived lives and developed into women who have far exceeded our fathers' wildest dreams!

Lacy

CHARMING CITRUS CHICKEN

....

PREP TIME 15 Minutes **COOK TIME** 15 Minutes

....

Chicken is a rich source of protein which is key to strengthening fragile hair. Protein also encourages positive hair growth.

1.5 lbs. Thin Cut Chicken Breast

1 Tablespoon Season All

1 Citrus Fruit (lemon, lime, or orange)

COOKING STEPS

1. Preheat oven at 350 degrees.

2. Place chicken cuts on a lined oiled baking sheet, sprinkle with season all and squeeze the citrus fruit of choice on the chicken cuts.

3. Bake for 15 minutes.

4. After 15 minutes, remove the chicken from the oven. Allow to cool, and enjoy!

SWEET AND SOUR QUINOA

....

PREP TIME 10 Minutes   **COOK TIME** 30 Minutes

....

Quinoa is very packed in protein. It strengthens, repairs, and helps maintain the color in our hair. The amino acids in quinoa also provide natural keratin, which helps to produce more hair follicles.

1 Pound Quinoa

1 Cup Blueberries

1/2 Fresh Lemon

1 Cup Cherry Tomatoes

1 Cup Peeled Cucumber

Dash Pink Salt

COOKING STEPS

1. In a medium saucepan, bring 4 cups of water to a boil.

2. Add 1 pound of quinoa to the boiled water.

3. Cook on medium heat for 20 minutes and occasionally stir to avoid the quinoa sticking to the pot.

4. Once cooked, change the heat setting to low.

5. Add blueberries, cherry tomatoes, peeled cucumbers, a dash of pink salt, squeeze lemon onto the quinoa and stir until consistent.

MS. HEALTHY HAIR SALAD

. . . .

PREP TIME 15 Minutes

. . . .

The healthy hair salad is packed with vitamins A and C,
and additional hair growth nutrients, including folate and iron.

6 Cups Baby Spinach

1 Cup Sliced Strawberries

2 Hard Boiled Eggs Chopped

1/3 Cup Feta Cheese

Honey Balsamic Dressing

1/4 Cup Vegetable Oil

1/2 Cup Balsamic Or White Wine Vinegar

1 Tablespoon Honey

COOKING STEPS

1. Add strawberries, chopped eggs, feta cheese, balsamic dressing, vegetable oil, your vinegar of choice, honey, and spinach to a mixing bowl.

2. Combine ingredients and toss.

3. Arrange salad toppings to your desire and enjoy!

Chef Charisma's
FINAL FOOD LOVE NOTE

Great energy creates exceptional food. The love you give your food is exactly what it will give in return. Know that you are in control, and treat each item with the love you'd like to taste.

Quality Woman

If I had to describe Charisma in one word, it would be LOYAL. Our sisterhood has been built on one specific principle: *family first, business second.* That family code has never been broken because our commitment to loyalty trumps everything.

I also love that Charisma *always* shows up. No matter what, she makes it a priority to show up for those she loves, and her presence always makes a difference. Whether it's an event or a family gathering, Charisma can show up for the last five minutes of the evening, and her special appearance can change the entire night. Her presence changes every atmosphere she walks into, and she's known to light up a room each and every time.

Lacy

Lacy's
FINAL HAIR LOVE NOTE

Quality Woman

If I had to describe Lacy in one word, it would be MULTIFACETED. She wears multiple hats and walks down many paths in life. Her ability to adapt is truly admirable.

Resilience is also one of Lacy's most remarkable qualities. I've watched her progression over the years in her professional career and personal life. As an entrepreneur, our lives are filled with trial and error, but no matter what, she's committed to reaching the success she desires and planned for her life.

Chef Charisma

"Healthy hair starts with a healthy scalp."

Self-Love is the greatest love that anyone can give themselves. God created us to be living creatures on earth with a purpose, and purpose starts with love and light. What's better than the love you give yourself when you cook yourself a delicious and healthy meal and the light and joy you experience after you're done? That's how our hair follicles feel once we've given them what they need to live and thrive!

Hair Food

DON'TS

Below is a list of foods we recommend removing from your diet to continue your healthy hair journey.

Alcohol
High Mercury Foods
Pasta
Refined Grains
White Breads

In addition, avoid a diet that:

Lacks Calcium
Low in Protein
Low in Vitamins (Zinc, Iron, B12)
High in Sugar

Special Note: Please consult your physician or a nutritionist before making any changes to your diet.

POTENTIAL HAIR LOSS SIGNS AND SYMPTOMS

Burning Scalp

Itchy Scalp

Layers of Sticky Dandruff

Pimples

Redness

Slow Hair Growth

Small Circles or Patches on Scalp

Tender Scalp

HAIR LOSS CONDITIONS

Alopecia: Alopecia is the medical term for hair loss.

"Alopecia can affect just your scalp or your entire body, and it can be temporary or permanent. It can be the result of heredity, hormonal changes, medical conditions or a normal part of aging."[1]

Alopecia Areata: Alopecia Areata is a hair loss condition caused by an immune deficiency that attacks hair follicles.

"Alopecia areata is a common autoimmune disorder that often results in unpredictable hair loss. In the majority of cases, hair falls out in small patches around the size of a quarter. For most people, the hair loss is nothing more than a few patches, though in some cases it can be more extreme."[2]

Central Centrifugal Cicatricial Alopecia (CCCA): CCCA is a scalp disease that causes hair loss in the crown area, high inflammation, and scarring on the scalp surface.

"CCCA is a disease characterized by permanent hair loss in the crown region of the scalp, inflammation, and scarring. It occurs almost exclusively in black women aged 30 to 55 years.[3]

The exact cause of CCCA is unclear but is thought to be due to various factors. These include a history of intense heat, tight hairstyles, or the application of chemical relaxers and dyes. These hair grooming practices could have occurred as far back as during childhood or teenage years. CCCA can also be triggered by the naturally curly shape of African hair follicles. CCCA affects some individuals with no history of tight or harsh hairstyles.

People with CCCA often have burning, itching, tenderness, or tiny bumps on the scalp. These usually occur on the top of the head and gradually spreads outward. In the early stage, there may be no visible hair loss or the hairs may be fragile, short, and broken."[4]

Chemotherapy-Induced Alopecia (CIA): Hair Loss Induced by Cancer: Chemotherapy-Induced Alopecia is hair loss induced by cancer treatments such as chemotherapy. In these people, hair can potentially grow back.

"Hair loss is a common side effect of cancer treatment. Hair loss can happen as a side effect of chemotherapy, targeted therapy, radiation therapy, or a stem cell (bone marrow) transplant. These cancer treatments can harm the cells that help hair grow. It can affect hair all over your body, including your head, face, arms, legs, underarms, and pubic area."[5]

Postpartum Hair Loss: Postpartum hair loss is a form of hair loss experienced by women shortly after pregnancy.

"Many new moms see noticeable hair loss a few months after having a baby. This is normal — and not true hair loss. Dermatologists refer to this condition as excessive hair shedding. The excessive shedding is caused by falling estrogen levels."[6]

Stress: Stress-induced hair loss is a form of hair loss caused by emotional and physical tension.

"Three types of hair loss can be associated with high-stress levels:

- Telogen effluvium. In telogen effluvium, significant stress pushes large numbers of hair follicles into a resting phase. Within a few months, affected hairs might fall out suddenly when simply combing or washing your hair.

- Trichotillomania. Trichotillomania is an irresistible urge to pull out hair from your scalp, eyebrows, or other areas of your body. Hair pulling can be a way of dealing with negative or uncomfortable feelings, such as stress, tension, loneliness, boredom, or frustration.

- Alopecia areata.[7] [8]

Traction Alopecia: Traction Alopecia is a hair loss condition caused by tension and consistent hair pulling, chemical damage, or unhealthy hair care.

"Traction alopecia is caused by repeated trauma to hair follicles or from pulling your hair back into tight hairstyles."[9]

A native of Washington, DC and Prince Georges County, MD —Chef Charisma specializes in infusing local culture into her luxurious dishes. Her culinary career began in 2005 at her family-owned restaurant, and she has held a host of management and front-of-house positions in various hotels and restaurants. Her years of experience have given her extensive knowledge of the food and beverage industry. In addition, her inherited and God-given talent, along with her eclectic personality, has led her to many successful collaborations with other talented chefs and celebrity clients.

Chef Charisma McLaughlin

Luxury Caterer. Private Chef.
Event Curator.

Connect with Chef Charisma for your catering needs at:

Instagram.com/chefcharismaa
Chefcharisma5@gmail.com

Lacy Fields

Hair Technician. Beauty Enthusiast.
Healthy Hair Expert.

If you're seeking answers and more help related to hair health and hair loss restoration —you can visit Lacy Fields and her trained staff at:

Therapeutique Salon and Spa
1401 Rockville Pike
Rockville, MD 20853
www.therapeutiquesalonspa.com

Lacy Fields is a beauty professional with over 20 years of experience in the hair industry. Lacy began her hair care journey at a very young age, and she always knew she wanted to bring something different to the industry. By the age of fourteen, Lacy knew she would be a full-time life-changer, and with her skills and determination, she was destined to take the beauty industry by storm. She received her cosmetology license at seventeen years of age and was behind her first stylist chair by nineteen. With over 11 years of experience in Trichology, she coined herself "Ms. Healthy Hair." She began instructing her clients to eat healthier diets and live healthy lifestyles, which leads to healthier hair. Lacy has treated over 50 women for hair loss issues. Those issues ranged from postpartum hair loss, stress-related hair loss, alopecia, alopecia areata, traction alopecia, CCCA, and more. With direct consultations, Lacy investigates her client's lifestyles, from each client's genetic background to current related issues. She then develops a personalized hair care regimen that includes diet changes and scalp treatments.

Lacy is also a salon owner and serial entrepreneur. Throughout her journey within the beauty and hair industries, she has worked in several pageants and D.C. and NYC Fashion Weeks. Lacy's skill set and determination also led her to travel abroad to Europe to learn more industry cutting techniques. Her background and determination to stay ahead of the curve gives her an edge, and the ability to keep up with industry trends. Her investments have allowed her to become a business/salon owner, educator, colorist, and master stylist. Her mission is to leave the world better than she found it while ensuring everyone has healthy hair! While performing behind the chair, her objective is to make her clients fall in love with themselves again by offering countless styles, chemical services, educational needs, and therapeutic relief.

For more information on hair loss prevention and remediation visit:

www.hairfoodbook.com

REFERENCES LIST

1. "Hair Loss." *Mayo Clinic,* Mayo Foundation for Medical Education and Research, 22 May 2020, https://www.mayoclinic.org/diseases-conditions/hair-loss/symptoms-causes/syc-20372926.

2. "Alopecia Areata: Causes, Symptoms, and Treatment." *Medical News Today,* MediLexicon International, https://www.medicalnewstoday.com/articles/70956.

3. Crystal Aguh, MD. "Central Centrifugal Cicatricial Alopecia." *JAMA Dermatology,* JAMA Network, 1 Sept. 2020, https://jamanetwork.com/journals/jamadermatology/fullarticle/2768748.

4. Rodney, Dr. "CCCA Hair Loss Treatment- Eternal Dermatology- Columbia MD." *Eternal Dermatology Columbia MD,* 21 Apr. 2021, https://eternaldermatology.com/ccca-alopecia-hair-loss-treatment/.

5. "Managing Physical Side Effects." *Cancer.Net,* 13 Oct. 2021, https://www.cancer.net/coping-with-cancer/physical-emotional-and-social-effects-cancer/managing-physical-side-effects?ref=driverlayer.com%2Fweb.

6. "Hair Loss in New Moms." *American Academy of Dermatology,* https://www.aad.org/public/diseases/hair-loss/insider/new-moms.

7. Daniel K. Hall-Flavin, M.D. "Can Stress Make You Lose Your Hair?" *Mayo Clinic*, Mayo Foundation for Medical Education and Research, 14 Sept. 2021, https://www.mayoclinic.org/healthy-lifestyle/stress-management/expert-answers/stress-and-hair-loss/faq-20057820.

8. Jay, Kitty. "Hair Loss: Cause, Treatment, Prevention, and More." *Healthline,* Healthline Media, 29 Mar. 2019, https://www.healthline.com/health/stress/stress-hair-loss.

9. "3 Traction Alopecia Treatment Options You Should Know." *WebMD*, https://www.webmd.com/connect-to-care/hair-loss/treatment-options-for-traction-alopecia.

Printed in the USA
CPSIA information can be obtained
at www.ICGtesting.com
CBHW040735140424
6815CB00051B/628